BIBLE FACTORY PRESS PRESENTS

BIBLE
BIBLE

GAMES & INSPIRATION 2003

📖 BIBLE

1–888–4–A–BIBLE (888–422–

D0424366

© 2001 by Barbour Publishing, Inc.

ISBN 1-58660-311-6

Published by Barbour Publishing, Inc., P.O. Box 719, Uhrichsville, Ohio 44683 http://www.barbourbooks.com

ecpa Member of the
Evangelical Christian
Publishers Association

Printed in the United States of America.

GREETINGS FROM BIBLE FACTORY OUTLET!

As you may have guessed from the name of our store, the Bible is a very important Book to us. We hope it's important to you, too.

Perhaps you already know the Bible as God's Word. Maybe you're hearing about it for the very first time. Whatever your starting point, you'll find information, inspiration, and plenty of fun in this little book that celebrates the world's all-time best-seller—the only Book that gives hope to the world, the only Book with the power to change peoples' lives.

Bible Games & Inspiration 2002 starts you off with some challenging crossword puzzles to test your Bible knowledge—or to get you into the Bible to find the answers! Following that is a section of Bible Promises—selected verses from God's Word on a number of important topics such as forgiveness, kindness, and truth. Next are more puzzles—Bible word searches this time—for your enjoyment. And, finally, you'll read some classic quotes on prayer, love, faith, and grace.

We hope you'll learn from and be entertained by *Bible Games & Inspiration 2002*. If you'd like to know more, please stop in again for Bibles and other Christian materials. (And don't forget the coupons in the back of the book!)

We look forward to seeing you next time at Bible Factory Outlet.

PUZZLE 1

ACROSS

1. Returning exiles, the children of _____ (Ezra 2:44)
6. Standoffish
11. _____ of refuge
12. Mother of Samuel
14. "_____ if!"
15. Encountered
17. Biblical pronoun
18. Latin abbr.
19. Made with yeast
23. Take a wrong turn
24. City where Isaac died (var., Genesis 35:27)
25. Physicians' group (abbr.)
26. Looked at
27. Greet
28. Gossips
30. Brother of Harnepher (1 Chronicles 7:36)
32. On the outside (prefix)
33. Son of Midian (Genesis 25:4)
35. O.T. minor prophet (abbr.)
38. Father of Azareel (Nehemiah 11:13)
40. More painful
42. Hearts, for one
43. Offering
46. Preposition
47. Hospital inits.
48. King Og's kingdom (Numbers 21)
49. Pronoun
50. Aka Belteshazzar
53. He prophesied bondage for Paul
55. Bear or bee
56. Included in the inheritance of the tribe of Asher (Joshua 19:27)

DOWN

1. He was "smote" by Jael
2. Clara Bow, the _____ Girl
3. City near Bethel
4. Part of the hemoglobin molecule
5. Wife of Joseph (Genesis 41)
6. "Say _____"
7. _____ it on
8. Single
9. _____ a roll
10. Prettier

11. City in Assyria (Genesis 10:11)
13. Cattle crowds
16. Arabian city (Isaiah 21)
20. Brother of Joab (1 Chronicles 2:16)
21. Assign worth to (arch.)
22. Palm or line
23. "He that hath a bountiful ____ shall be blessed" (Proverbs 22:9)
26. Son of Zerahiah (Ezra 8:4)
29. Relative of a borough (abbr.)
31. Son of Jether (1 Chronicles 7:38)
33. Alleviated
34. Servant of Gideon (Judges 7:10)
36. Middle Eastern language (abbr.)
37. City in the inheritance of the children of Simeon (Joshua 19:4)
39. Southern European country
40. His son Jonathan served in David's army (1 Chronicles 11:34)
41. Asiatic deer (pl.)
44. Linking verb
45. Comparative conjunction
48. Get-together, for a purpose
51. Favorite first word?
52. Preposition
54. Command word

ACROSS

1. Priestly garments
5. "Except your righteousness shall ____ the righteousness of the scribes" (Matthew 5:20)
7. Linking verb
8. Replied
10. "Give unto the Lord the glory ____ unto his name" (Psalm 29:2)
11. "Can a maid forget her ornaments, or a bride her ____?" (Jeremiah 2:32)
13. Of flying (comb. form)
14. Son of Seth
15. "Israel did ____ manna forty years" (Exodus 16:35)
17. "Yea, the ____ hath found an house" (Psalm 84:3)
19. "Employer" of Hagar
21. Oft-used abbr.
22. One (Ger.)
23. Rate of speed (abbr.)
24. Where Montauk is (abbr.)
25. "All they that cast ____ into the brooks shall lament" (Isaiah 19:8)
27. "They ____ in thee, and were not confounded" (Psalm 22:5)
29. "Agnus ___"
30. Pay attention
31. "Yet will I bring ____ plague more upon Pharaoh" (Exodus 11:1)
32. "____ ye, and believe the gospel" (Mark 1:15)
34. "And Nathan said to David, Thou ____ the man" (2 Samuel 12:7)
35. End or line
36. John, to a Scot
37. "He made a ____ about the altar" (1 Kings 18:32)
39. "He shall be like a ____ planted by the rivers" (Psalm 1:3)

DOWN

1. Chopping tool
2. Public national library (abbr.)
3. "Upon these we ____ more abundant honour" (1 Corinthians 12:23)
4. "He hath put down the mighty from their ____" (Luke 1:52)
5. Before (poet.)
6. 502, according to Cicero
7. Charismatic atmosphere
9. God spoke in Bible times through these
10. Rely

11. Immediately (arch.)
12. Serving of corn
13. "All they which dwelt in ____ heard the word of the Lord Jesus" (Acts 19:10)
14. Great Lake
16. "I was afraid, and went and hid thy ____ in the earth" (Matthew 25:25)
18. Trusted, with "upon"
19. Potato
20. "I flee unto thee to ____ me" (Psalm 143:9)
23. "____ not thyself because of evildoers" (Psalm 37:1)
26. European language (abbr.)
27. "Leah was ____ eyed" (Genesis 29:17)
28. Ripped
30. "If thou seek him with all thy ____" (Deuteronomy 4:29)
33. Favorite
34. Sighing sound
36. "He casteth forth his ____ like morsels" (Psalm 147:17)
38. Compass dir.

PUZZLE 3

ACROSS

1. She played Nora to Powell's Nick
4. Balaam's bane
7. Father of Saul (Acts 13)
10. Mimic
11. O.T. book (abbr.)
12. "Through faith also ____. . .received strength to conceive" (Hebrews 11:11)
13. One quality of God
16. Like blustery, cold weather
17. First manners lesson word
18. Grain
20. Title given to Italian monk
21. "Blessed are they whose. . .sins are ____" (Romans 4:7)
25. Depressed
27. "I ____ on the work of thy hands" (Psalm 143:5)
28. Christmas ____
29. Girl (Scot.)
30. Found in veins
31. ____ canto, singing style
32. Shoshonean
33. ____ Scott decision, landmark legal case
34. Roll call answer
35. "who hath ____ of eyes?" (Proverbs 23:29)
37. Seasoning (Fr.)
38. Shoe width
39. Heats to almost boiling
42. "The Lord said unto him [Solomon], I have heard thy prayer and thy ____" (1 Kings 9:3)
45. Retirement accts.
46. Its members trace their ancestors to the Mayflower (abbr.)
47. Plain of ____ (Nehemiah 6:2)
48. Kin (abbr.)
49. Consumed
50. ____ Paltz, NY

DOWN

1. "Thy word is a ____ unto my feet" (Psalm 119:105)
2. European auto maker
3. "Because I have called, and ____ ____" (2 words, Proverbs 1:24)
4. Feminine name (var.)
5. Ump's call
6. Texas college (abbr.)
7. ____ blanche

8. Gershwin
9. Maxim; proverb
14. "Lest at any time your hearts be overcharged with. . .____ of this life" (Luke 21:34)
15. Let free
19. Park, for one (abbr.)
21. "Behold, I cast out devils, and I do ____" (Luke 13:32)
22. "For ____ is as the sin of witchcraft" (1 Samuel 15:23)
23. At any time
24. Editor's mark
25. To obscure
26. Fashionably ____
27. "Let me set a ____ of bread before thee" (1 Samuel 28:22)
33. "Praise the Lord from the earth, ye dragons, and all ____" (Psalm 148:7)
34. Miami pro team
36. Himalayan country
37. Give goosebumps
39. Scram!
40. Finished
41. "Drought and heat consume the ____ waters" (Job 24:19)
42. Title of respect
43. Actress Mary
44. Director Lupino

PUZZLE 4

ACROSS

1. "They came to the threshing-floor of ____, which is beyond Jordan" (Genesis 50:10)
5. Highway (abbr.)
8. Bargain events
10. ____ apple (candy flavor)
11. "After the same manner also he took the cup, when he had ____" (1 Corinthians 11:25)
13. Beyond compare
15. Paddle
16. Momentous sign
17. ___-Eglaim, near the Salt Sea (Ezekiel 47)
18. Wight, for one
19. *King* ____ (J. Clavell novell)
20. Went golfing
21. "The Lord is good to ____" (Psalm 145:9)
24. Compass dir.
25. Like some numbers
26. ____ bargain
27. "These shall ye not eat of them that chew the ____" (Leviticus 11:4)
28. Minor prophet
29. Conjunction
30. "For we are saved by ____" (Romans 8:24)
34. "He it is, to whom I shall give a ____, when I have dipped it" (John 13:26)
35. "They shall lay hands on the sick, and they shall ____" (Mark 16:18)
37. Entrapped
40. "So be it"
41. "When he had made a scourge. . .he ____ them all out of the temple" (John 2:15)
42. David ___-Gurion
43. Action

DOWN

1. Was in agreement
2. Greek letter
3. Mount Blanc is one
4. "He [Nebuchadnezzar] was ____ from his kingly throne" (Daniel 5:20)
5. Stronger than string
6. "Whosoever shall smite thee on thy right cheek, __ to him the other" (Matthew 5:39)

7. Poetic before
9. "Ye were _____ with that holy Spirit of promise" (Ephesians 1:13)
10. "How precious also are thy thoughts. . .how great is the _____ of them" (Psalm 139:17)
12. _____ Scott, subject of landmark legal case
13. Hence
14. Dry or liquid
18. Judge Lance
19. Taped
21. "I see a rod of an _____ tree" (Jeremiah 1:11)
22. "The _____ shall lie down with the kid" (Isaiah 11:6)
23. _____ Cruces, NM
26. Bridge response
30. "Whilst we are at _____ in the body, we are absent from the Lord" (2 Corinthians 5:6)
31. "God so clothe the grass. . .which to day is, and to morrow is cast into the _____" (Matthew 6:30)
32. "I will not with ink and _____ write unto thee" (3 John 13)
33. Hesitation sound
36. NYC sight
38. "Let her be as the loving hind and the pleasant _____" (Proverbs 5:19)
39. First female

PUZZLE 5

ACROSS

1. Kitchen measure (abbr.)
4. "Let her ___: against the day of my burying hath she kept this" (John 12:7)
9. Baden-Baden is one
12. Titian's medium
14. "I have set before thee an ____ door" (Revelation 3:8)
15. Possesses
16. Evening wrap
18. "The ear trieth words, as the mouth ____ meat" (Job 34:3)
20. Strive for dominance
21. Rows
22. Hardly worth commenting on
26. "Leah said a troop cometh: and she called his name ____" (Genesis 30:11)
27. Actor Auberjonois
28. "They were swifter than eagles, they were stronger than ____" (2 Samuel 1:23)
30. Preposition
32. Univ. subj.
33. Collect collectibles
34. Verses to a Grecian urn
35. French conjunction
36. Diagram
37. Author unknown (abbr.)
38. Exclamation of achievement
39. "Thou ____ up the sum, full of wisdom" (Ezekiel 28:12)
41. Live like a longhorn
43. Leave out
44. Where a ship is secured
46. Lake ____ (outdoor playground)
49. Hosp. facilities (pl.)
50. Affirm or attest to
52. Delhi "to go" garb
53. Born (Fr.)
54. African scavenger
55. Author Amy

DOWN

1. Basketball blunders (abbr.)
2. Portraitist's command
3. "He was ____ with twelve yoke of oxen" (1 Kings 19:19)
5. KJV exclamation
6. Elect
7. Spiffy
8. Certain sailors
9. Broken piece of pottery, KJV style

10. Touches lightly
11. Tree type
13. Demetrius, in *The Robe*
17. The family of ____, descendants of Gad (Numbers 26:16)
19. Prince of Wales, and others
22. "I give to eat of the ____ of life" (Revelation 2:7)
23. Torn apart
24. Feminine name
25. Ananias and Sapphira, to name two
29. Bones (comb. form)
30. Big deals
31. Abraham's abode
33. Son of Ahab (1 Kings 22:40)
34. "He that. . .meddleth with strife. . .is like ____ ____ [2 words] taketh a dog by the ears" (Proverbs 26:17)
36. Scorch
37. Witness Protection Program gift
38. Was no longer supine
40. Quantity (abbr.)
41. Former senator from Tennessee
42. Green monster
44. Door designation
45. Command to a horse
47. Mouth (pl.)
48. German article
51. TLC provider

ACROSS

1. "God clave an hollow place that was in the ____, and there came water thereout" (Judges 15:19)
4. Prepare fruit
8. Whatever ____ you
12. Jurist Fortas
13. Black
14. Dagger
15. "He ____ my strength in the way" (Psalm 102:23)
17. Permanent mark
18. Evidence of beating
19. Sesame, for one
20. Northwest ____ (abbr.)
21. "Shoot out thine ____, and destroy them" (Psalm 144:6)
24. Ate out
27. Linking verb
28. Comprehend
29. Son of Zeus
30. "How can a man be born when he is ___?" (John 3:4)
31. *Dead* ____ (Dick Francis classic)
32. French pronoun
33. Hole-making tool
34. Amusement park amusements
35. Begin a conversation
37. Wager
38. Hurry (arch.)
39. Punish (arch.)
43. Steakhouse selection, perhaps
45. "Though they would have cast anchors out of the ____" (Acts 27:30)
47. Cary Grant, once
48. Father of Azariah (2 Chronicles 15:1)
49. Paris summer
50. Challenge
51. Whirlpool
52. Affirmative vote

DOWN

1. Spielberg film
2. Aid's partner
3. ____ thin
4. "There was none that moved the wing or opened the mouth, or ____" (Isaiah 10:14)
5. Son of Ner (2 Samuel 2:8)
6. "Asahel was as light of foot as a wild ____" (2 Samuel 2:18)
7. Like omega
8. Son of Kohath (1 Chronicles 6:22)

A crossword grid with numbered cells: 1, 2, 3, 4, 5, 6, 7, 8, 9, 10, 11 (top row); 12, 13, 14; 15, 16, 17; 18, 19; 20, 21, 22, 23; 24, 25, 26, 27, 28; 29, 30, 31; 32, 33, 34; 35, 36, 37; 38, 39, 40, 41, 42; 43, 44, 45, 46; 47, 48, 49; 50, 51, 52.

9. "And they wrought onyx stones ____ in ouches of gold" (Exodus 39:6)
10. Bucolic locale
11. Indian weight
16. Unclean birds (Deuteronomy 14:13)
19. Pay dirt
21. Son of Bela (Numbers 26:40)
22. Used to be
23. Cupboard collections, as in dishes
24. Fruit of the palm
25. Smooth
26. One close by
27. Cheer competitor
30. "____ no man any thing, but to love" (Romans 13:8)
31. Refers to
33. Mature
34. "The wrath of the Lord arose against his people, till there was no ____" (2 Chronicles 36:16)
36. Seat location
37. Told all
40. Feminine name
41. Bethlehem: ____ of David
42. Fencing gear
43. Exterminate
44. Lupino
45. Nemesis
46. "The ____ number. . .is to be redeemed" (Numbers 3:48)

Puzzle 7

ACROSS

1. "What _____ I am afraid, I will trust in thee" (Psalm 56:3)
5. "They cast _____; that is, the lot, before Haman" (Esther 3:7)
8. It's not exactly red
12. In the near future (arch.)
13. Gobbled up
14. First two words in Key's composition
15. "Help thou mine _____" (Mark 9:24)
17. *Au* _____ (teenaged helper)
18. Relieve
19. Filled with evil desires, as a heart
21. Synonym for scow
24. Toward the sheltered side
25. "_____ them that have the rule over you" (Hebrews 13:17)
26. "Thou hast _____ me when I was in distress" (Psalm 4:1)
30. Legal object
31. Michael, for one
32. Poem
33. "Yea, I _____ unto you, and. . .none of you that convinced Job" (Job 32:12)
35. Zone
36. Beverages
37. Squander
38. Cyrus was the king of _____ (Ezra 3:7)
41. One who hisses
42. Skirt feature
43. "Be sober, be _____" (1 Peter 5:8)
48. Melita, for one
49. Natural mineral
50. Day before (pl.)
51. Samuel, to some
52. See _____
53. Want no more

DOWN

1. Greek letter
2. Holiday, for one
3. Multitude
4. Strength
5. Receipt word
6. Western Native American
7. What the watchful waiter did?
8. Mines found on Cyprus
9. Dweller in the land of Seir, the country of Edom (Genesis 32:3)
10. Depilatory brand

11. Seaport in Lebanon
16. Recline
20. Repast
21. Fierce wind of the Adriatic
22. Aid's ally
23. What's left
24. Heavenly beings (Fr.)
26. Earnest attempt
27. Blood and guts
28. Utopia
29. "If we be _____ with Christ. . .we shall also live with him" (Romans 6:8)
31. Girl's nickname
34. Resurrection day
35. "A word fitly spoken is like _____ of gold" (Proverbs 25:11)
37. Supplemental income (abbr.)
38. Greek letters
39. Word in a threat
40. Stir up
41. Long in the tooth
44. Anger
45. Actress Gardner
46. Fish trap
47. Double this for (perhaps) fatal flier

CROSSWORD
ANSWERS

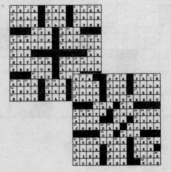

Puzzle 1

	S	I	A	H	A		A	L	O	O	F
C	I	T	I	E	S		H	A	N	N	A H
A	S			M	E	T		Y	E		I E
L	E	A	V	E	N	E	D			E	R R
A	R	B	A		A	M	A		E	Y	E D
H	A	I	L		T	A	T	T	L	E	R S
		S	U	A	H		E	P	I		
E	P	H	E	R				H	A	B	
A	H	A	S	A	I		S	O	R	E	R
S	U	I	T		T	I	T	H	E		T O
E	R		B	A	S	H	A	N		H	E
D	A	N	I	E	L		A	G	A	B	U S
	H	O	N	E	Y		N	E	I	E	L

Puzzle 2

		A	L	B	S		
E	X	C	E	E	D		
A	R	E		S	A	I	D
D	U	E		A	T	T	I R E
A	E R		E	N	O	S		E A T
S	P	A	R	R	O	W		S A R A H
I	E		E	I	N		F	P M		L I
A	N	G	L	E		T	R	U	S	T E D
D	E I		H	E	E	D		O N E
R	E	P	E	N	T		A R T
	D	E	A	D		I A N
	T	R	E	N	C	H	
	T	R	E	E			

Puzzle 3

L O Y		A S S		C I S
A P E	L A M		S A R A
M E R C I F U L		R A W
P L E A S E		O A T
	F R A	C O V E R E D
B L U E	M U S E	E V E
L A S S	O R E		B E L
U T E	D R E D	H E R E
R E D N E S S		S E L
	E E E	S C A L D S
S U P P L I C A T I O N
I R A S	D A R	O N O
R E L	A T E	N E W

Puzzle 4

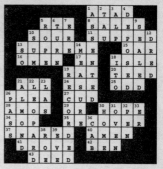

	A T A D
R T E	S A L E S
S O U R	S U P P E D
S U P R E M E	O A R
O M E N	E N	I S L E
	R A T	T E E D
A L L	E S E	O D D
P L E A	C U D
A M O S	O R	H O P E
S O P	R E C O V E R
S N A R E D	A M E N
D R O V E	B E N
D E E D

Puzzle 5

T S P	A L O N E	S P A
O I L S	O P E N	H A S
S T O L E	T A S T E T H
W A R	T I E R S
T R I V I A L	G A D
R E N E	L I O N S	A T
E N G	A M A S S	O D E
E T	C H A R T	A N O N
A H A	S E A L E S T
G R A Z E	O M I T
M O O R I N G	T A H O E
E R S	A V E R	S A R I
N E E	H Y E N A	T A N

Puzzle 6

J A W	P A R E	A I L S
A B E	E B O N	S N E E
W E A K E N E D	S C A R
S T R I P E	O I L
T E R	A R R O W S
D I N E D	A R E	S E E
A R E S	O L D	C E R T
T O I	A W L	R I D E S
E N G A G E	B E T
H I E	A M E R C E
R I B S	F O R E S H I P
I D O L	O D E D	E T E
D A R E	E D D Y	A Y E

Puzzle 7

T I M E	P U R	C E N T
A N O N	A T E	O S A Y
U N B E L I E F	P A I R
R I D	I M P U R E
B A R G E	A L E E
O B E Y	E N L A R G E D
R E S	A N G E L	O D E
A T T E N D E D	A R E A
A D E S	S P E N D
P E R S I A	A S P
S L I T	V I G I L A N T
I S L E	O R E	R V E S
S E E R	R E D	S A T E

Bible Promises on
Adversity

For I reckon that the sufferings of this present time are not worthy to be compared with the glory which shall be revealed in us.   *Romans 8:18*

These things I have spoken unto you, that in me ye might have peace. In the world ye shall have tribulation: but be of good cheer; I have overcome the world.   *John 16:33*

But what things were gain to me, those I counted loss for Christ. Yea doubtless, and I count all things but loss for the excellency of the knowledge of Christ Jesus my Lord: for whom I have suffered the loss of all things, and do count them but dung, that I may win Christ, and be found in him. . .
    That I may know him, and the power of his resurrection, and the fellowship of his sufferings, being made conformable unto his death; If by any means I might attain unto the resurrection of the dead.   *Philippians 3:7–11*

The righteous cry, and the LORD heareth, and delivereth them out of all their troubles.   *Psalm 34:17*

But the God of all grace, who hath called us unto his eternal glory by Christ Jesus, after that ye have suffered a while, make you perfect, stablish, strengthen, settle you.
                                                        1 Peter 5:10

Blessed are ye, when men shall hate you, and when they shall separate you from their company, and shall reproach you, and cast out your name as evil, for the Son of man's sake.   *Luke 6:22*

Bible Promises on
Charity

But when thou makest a feast, call the poor, the maimed, the lame, the blind: And thou shalt be blessed; for they cannot recompense thee: for thou shalt be recompensed at the resurrection of the just.   *Luke 14:13–14*

He that despiseth his neighbour sinneth: but he that hath mercy on the poor, happy is he.   *Proverbs 14:21*

I have shewed you all things, how that so labouring ye ought to support the weak, and to remember the words of the Lord Jesus, how he said, It is more blessed to give than to receive.   *Acts 20:35*

Give, and it shall be given unto you; good measure, pressed down, and shaken together, and running over, shall men give into your bosom. For with the same measure that ye mete withal it shall be measured to you again.   *Luke 6:38*

Above all things have fervent charity among yourselves: for charity shall cover the multitude of sins. Use hospitality one to another without grudging. As every man hath received the gift, even so minister the same one to another, as good stewards of the manifold grace of God.   *1 Peter 4:8–10*

I have been young, and now am old; yet have I not seen the righteous forsaken, nor his seed begging bread. He is ever merciful, and lendeth; and his seed is blessed.
                    Psalm 37:25–26

BIBLE PROMISES ON
COURAGE

Wait on the LORD: be of good courage, and he shall strengthen thine heart: wait, I say, on the LORD.

Psalm 27:14

For God hath not given us the spirit of fear; but of power, and of love, and of a sound mind. *2 Timothy 1:7*

So that we may boldly say, The Lord is my helper, and I will not fear what man shall do unto me. *Hebrews 13:6*

The wicked flee when no man pursueth: but the righteous are bold as a lion. *Proverbs 28:1*

In whom we have boldness and access with confidence by the faith of him. *Ephesians 3:12*

Having therefore, brethren, boldness to enter into the holiest by the blood of Jesus. *Hebrews 10:19*

Watch ye, stand fast in the faith, quit you like men, be strong. *1 Corinthians 16:13*

BIBLE PROMISES ON
ETERNITY

In my Father's house are many mansions: if it were not so, I would have told you. I go to prepare a place for you. And if I go and prepare a place for you, I will come again, and receive you unto myself; that where I am, there ye may be also.
John 14:2–3

And I give unto them eternal life; and they shall never perish, neither shall any man pluck them out of my hand.
John 10:28

For the wages of sin is death; but the gift of God is eternal life through Jesus Christ our Lord.
Romans 6:23

And this is the record, that God hath given to us eternal life, and this life is in his Son.
1 John 5:11

Search the scriptures; for in them ye think ye have eternal life: and they are they which testify of me.
John 5:39

And many of them that sleep in the dust of the earth shall awake, some to everlasting life, and some to shame and everlasting contempt.
Daniel 12:2

BIBLE PROMISES ON
FORGIVENESS

And be ye kind one to another, tenderhearted, forgiving one another, even as God for Christ's sake hath forgiven you.
Ephesians 4:32

And when ye stand praying, forgive, if ye have ought against any: that your Father also which is in heaven may forgive you your trespasses.

But if ye do not forgive, neither will your Father which is in heaven forgive your trespasses.　*Mark 11:25–26*

And forgive us our sins; for we also forgive every one that is indebted to us. And lead us not into temptation; but deliver us from evil.　*Luke 11:4*

Forbearing one another, and forgiving one another, if any man have a quarrel against any: even as Christ forgave you, so also do ye.　*Colossians 3:13*

The discretion of a man deferreth his anger; and it is his glory to pass over a transgression.　*Proverbs 19:11*

Judge not, and ye shall not be judged: condemn not, and ye shall not be condemned: forgive, and ye shall be forgiven.
Luke 6:37

Bible Promises on
Friendship

A man that hath friends must shew himself friendly: and there is a friend that sticketh closer than a brother.

Proverbs 18:24

Which off you shall have a friend, and shall go unto him at midnight, and say unto him, Friend, lend me three loaves; For a friend of mine in his journey is come to me, and I have nothing to set before him? And he from within shall answer and say. . .I cannot rise and give thee. I say unto you Though he will not rise and give him, because he is his friend, yet because of his importunity he will rise and give him as many as he needeth.

Luke 11:5–8

A friend loveth at all times.

Proverbs 17:17

Faithful are the wounds of a friend.

Proverbs 27:6

Whosoever therefore will be a friend of the world is the enemy of God.

James 4:4

Iron sharpeneth iron; so a man sharpeneth the countenance of his friend.

Proverbs 27:17

BIBLE PROMISES ON
GENTLENESS

Take my yoke upon you, and learn of me; for I am meek
and lowly in heart: and ye shall find rest unto your souls.
Matthew 11:29

But the meek shall inherit the earth; and shall delight
themselves in the abundance of peace.   *Psalm 37:11*

He shall feed his flock like a shepherd: he shall gather the
lambs with his arm, and carry them in his bosom, and shall
gently lead those that are with young.   *Isaiah 40:11*

But the fruit of the Spirit is love, joy, peace, longsuffering,
gentleness, goodness, faith.   *Galatians 5:22*

But the wisdom that is from above is first pure, then peace-
able, gentle, and easy to be intreated, full of mercy and
good fruits, without partiality, and without hypocrisy.
James 3:17

But we were gentle among you, even as a nurse cherisheth
her children: So being affectionately desirous of you, we
were willing to have imparted unto you, not the gospel of
God only, but also our own souls.   *1 Thessalonians 2:7–8*

BIBLE PROMISES ON
GOD'S LOVE

Behold, what manner of love the Father hath bestowed upon us, that we should be called the sons of God.

1 John 3:1

For I am persuaded, that neither death, nor life, nor angels, nor principalities, nor powers, nor things present, nor things to come, nor height, nor depth, nor any other creature, shall be able to separate us from the love of God, which is in Christ Jesus our Lord. *Romans 8:38–39*

For God so loved the world, that he gave his only begotten Son, that whosoever believeth in him should not perish, but have everlasting life. *John 3:16*

I will heal their backsliding, I will love them freely: for mine anger is turned away from him. *Hosea 14:4*

In this was manifested the love of God toward us, because that God sent his only begotten Son into the world, that we might live through him. *1 John 4:9*

BIBLE PROMISES ON
HONESTY

Finally, brethren, whatsoever things are true, whatsoever things are honest, whatsoever things are just, whatsoever things are pure, whatsoever things are lovely, whatsoever things are of good report; if there be any virtue, and if there be any praise, think on these things.

Philippians 4:8

Pray for us: for we trust we have a good conscience, in all things willing to live honestly.   *Hebrews 13:18*

That ye study to be quiet, and to do your own business, and to work with your own hands. . .That ye may walk honestly toward them that are without, and that ye may have lack of nothing.   *1 Thessalonians 4:11–12*

Be of the same mind one toward another. . . . Recompense to no man evil for evil. Provide things honest in the sight of all men.   *Romans 12:16–17*

Lie not one to another, seeing that ye have put off the old man with his deeds; And have put on the new man, which is renewed in knowledge after the image of him that created him.   *Colossians 3:9–10*

BIBLE PROMISES ON
HUMILITY

Whosoever therefore shall humble himself as this little child, the same is greatest in the kingdom of heaven.

Matthew 18:4

If I must needs glory, I will glory of the things which concern mine infirmities. *2 Corinthians 11:30*

The fear of the LORD is the instruction of wisdom; and before honour is humility. *Proverbs 15:33*

Yea, all of you be subject one to another, and be clothed with humility: for God resisteth the proud, and giveth grace to the humble. Humble yourselves therefore under the mighty hand of God, that he may exalt you in due time.

1 Peter 5:5–6

But he giveth more grace. Wherefore he saith, God resisteth the proud, but giveth grace unto the humble. *James 4:6*

By humility and the fear of the LORD are riches, and honour, and life. *Proverbs 22:4*

BIBLE PROMISES ON
KINDNESS

She openeth her mouth with wisdom; and in her tongue is the law of kindness. *Proverbs 31:26*

And to godliness brotherly kindness; and to brotherly kindness charity. For if these things be in you, and abound. . .ye shall neither be barren nor unfruitful in the knowledge of our Lord Jesus Christ. *2 Peter 1:7–8*

As we have therefore opportunity, let us do good unto all men, especially unto them who are of the household of faith. *Galatians 6:10*

The desire of a man is his kindness: and a poor man is better than a liar. The fear of the LORD tendeth to life: and he that hath it shall abide satisfied. *Proverbs 19:22–23*

And if ye lend to them of whom ye hope to receive, what thank have ye? for sinners also lend to sinners, to receive as much again. But love ye your enemies, and do good, and lend, hoping for nothing again; and your reward shall be great, and ye shall be the children of the Highest: for he is kind unto the unthankful and to the evil. *Luke 6:34–35*

BIBLE PROMISES ON
REPENTANCE

The Lord is not slack concerning his promise, as some men count slackness; but is longsuffering to us-ward, not willing that any should perish, but that all should come to repentance.   *2 Peter 3:9*

I will have mercy, and not sacrifice: for I am not come to call the righteous, but sinners to repentance.

Matthew 9:13

Likewise, I say unto you, there is joy in the presence of the angels of God over one sinner that repenteth.

Luke 15:10

The time is fulfilled, and the kingdom of God is at hand: repent ye, and believe the gospel.   *Mark 1:15*

And the times of this ignorance God winked at; but now commandeth all men every where to repent.   *Acts 17:30*

He that covereth his sins shall not prosper: but whoso confesseth and forsaketh them shall have mercy.

Proverbs 28:13

BIBLE PROMISES ON
RIGHTEOUSNESS

Blessed are they which do hunger and thirst after righteousness: for they shall be filled.   *Matthew 5:6*

LORD, who shall abide in thy tabernacle? who shall dwell in thy holy hill?
He that walketh uprightly, and worketh righteousness, and speaketh the truth in his heart.   *Psalm 15:1–2*

But seek ye first the kingdom of God, and his righteousness; and all these things shall be added unto you.
          Matthew 6:33

He withdraweth not his eyes from the righteous: but with kings are they on the throne; yea, he doth establish them for ever, and they are exalted.   *Job 36:7*

For he hath made him to be sin for us, who knew no sin; that we might be made the righteousness of God in him.
          2 Corinthians 5:21

If we confess our sins, he is faithful and just to forgive us our sins, and to cleanse us from all unrighteousness.
          1 John 1:9

BIBLE PROMISES ON
SEEKING GOD

Sow to yourselves in righteousness, reap in mercy; break up your fallow ground: for it is time to seek the LORD, till he come and rain righteousness upon you.   *Hosea 10:12*

Seek the LORD, and ye shall live.   *Amos 5:6*

And ye shall seek me, and find me, when ye shall search for me with all your heart.   *Jeremiah 29:13*

With my soul have I desired thee in the night; yea, with my spirit within me will I seek thee early: for when thy judgments are in the earth, the inhabitants of the world will learn righteousness.   *Isaiah 26:9*

And I say unto you, Ask, and it shall be given you; seek, and ye shall find; knock, and it shall be opened unto you.
          Luke 11:9

But if from thence thou shalt seek the LORD thy God, thou shalt find him, if thou seek him with all thy heart and with all thy soul.   *Deuteronomy 4:29*

Bible Promises on
Temptation

Let no man say when he is tempted, I am tempted of God: for God cannot be tempted with evil, neither tempteth he any man. *James 1:13*

And lead us not into temptation, but deliver us from evil: For thine is the kingdom, and the power, and the glory, for ever. Amen. *Matthew 6:13*

And when he was at the place, he said unto them, Pray that ye enter not into temptation. *Luke 22:40*

There hath no temptation taken you but such as is common to man: but God is faithful, who will not suffer you to be tempted above that ye are able; but will with the temptation also make a way to escape, that ye may be able to bear it. *1 Corinthians 10:13*

The Lord knoweth how to deliver the godly out of temptations. *2 Peter 2:9*

Because thou hast kept the word of my patience, I also will keep thee from the hour of temptation, which shall come upon all the world, to try them that dwell upon the earth. *Revelation 3:10*

BIBLE PROMISES ON
TRUTH

Buy the truth, and sell it not; also wisdom, and instruction, and understanding.   *Proverbs 23:23*

For the LORD is good; his mercy is everlasting; and his truth endureth to all generations.   *Psalm 100:5*

Jesus saith unto him, I am the way, the truth, and the life: no man cometh unto the Father, but by me.   *John 14:6*

These are the things that ye shall do; Speak ye every man the truth to his neighbour; execute the judgment of truth and peace in your gates.   *Zechariah 8:16*

For the law was given by Moses, but grace and truth came by Jesus Christ.   *John 1:17*

He is the Rock, his work is perfect: for all his ways are judgment: a God of truth and without iniquity, just and right is he.   *Deuteronomy 32:4*

1 Corinthians 13

BEHAVE	MAN
CHARITY	MEN
CHILDISH THINGS	MYSTERIES
ENDURETH	NEVER FAILETH
ENVIETH NOT	NOT PUFFED UP
FACE TO FACE	REMOVE MOUNTAINS
FAITH	SOUNDING BRASS
GIFT OF PROPHECY	SUFFERETH LONG
GREATEST	THINKETH NO EVIL
HOPETH	THROUGH A GLASS
INIQUITY	TINKLING CYMBAL
KIND	TONGUES
KNOWLEDGE	TRUTH

```
S Y C E H P O R P F O T F I G
N C T D S T S E T A E R G H N
I J H N S E O F A I T H E T O
A M I I A S U H T U R T C E L
T I N K L I N G C Y M B A L H
N E K N G D D M N H E T F I T
U N E O A E I Y A O N Y O A E
O V T W H N N S C P T T T F R
M I H L G D G T H E B I E R E
E E N E U U B E A T E U C E F
V T O D O R R R R H H Q A V F
O H E G R E A I I N A I F E U
M N V E H T S E T A V N N N S
E O I U T H S S Y M E I F G G
R T L P U D E F F U P T O N S
```

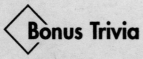

Bonus Trivia

Who said, "Within 100 years of my death, the Bible will be extinct?"

Praise!!

ADORE	OBEY
BLESS	OFFER
BREATHE	PERFECT
CONTINUALLY	SACRIFICE
EXALT	SEVEN TIMES
EXTOL	SHOUT
GIVE	SING
GLORIFY	SPEAK
HEAVEN AND EARTH	THANKSGIVING
HEIGHTS	WAIT
HONOR	WORKS
LEAP	WORTHY
LOVE	

```
S K R O W G I V E B V B G E G
D H C S E M I T N E V E S C K
P A E L N E Q S H V L Q I G X
Y L L A U N I T N O C D N N Y
W X B F V I A W T L A S G I K
S T H G I E H E X T O L I V S
E L F C R H N V E Q P N G I L
C Y E B O C T A I Y E A Y G I
I W O N F D R Y N C R Z Q S W
F V O E F E F W F D F B D K O
I R S A E I X A K A E P S N R
R Z S D R Z A A T A C A X A T
C U E O A G H Q L V T K R H H
A B L R E S H O U T F D S T Y
S G B E W A I T M W H Z Z T H
```

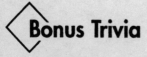

Characteristics
of Christ

ALIVE	JUST
BENEVOLENT	LOVING
COMPASSIONATE	MEEK
DISCERNING	MERCIFUL
FAITHFUL	POWER
FORGIVING	RIGHTEOUS
GENTLE	SERVES
GOOD	SINLESS
GUILELESS	SPOTLESS
HARMLESS	TEACHES
HEALS	TRUE
HELPING	WISE
HOLY	ZEALOUS
HUMBLE	

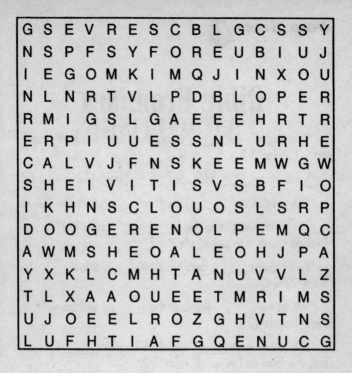

```
G S E V R E S C B L G C S S Y
N S P F S Y F O R E U B I U J
I E G O M K I M Q J I N X O U
N L N R T V L P D B L O P E R
R M I G S L G A E E H R T R
E R P I U U E S S N L U R H E
C A L V J F N S K E E M W G W
S H E I V I T I S V S B F I O
I K H N S C L O U O S L S R P
D O O G E R E N O L P E M Q C
A W M S H E O A L E O H J P A
Y X K L C M H T A N U V V L Z
T L X A A O U E E T M R I M S
U J O E E L R O Z G H V T N S
L U F H T I A F G Q E N U C G
```

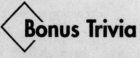

Bible Promises

"Casting all your _____ upon Him, for He careth for you." 1 Peter 5:7.

"I will never _____ thee, nor _____ thee." Hebrews 13:5.

"The Lord is my _____, I shall not _____." Psalm 23:1.

"_____ thy way unto the _____; _____ also in Him, and He shall bring it to pass." Psalm 37:5.

"Be of good _____, and He shall _____ thine _____." Psalm 27:14.

"When thou _____ through the _____, I will be with thee." Isaiah 43:2.

"When He shall _____, we shall be like _____, for we shall see Him as He is." 1 John 3:2.

"Be not _____, for I am thy God." Isaiah 41:10.

"He giveth _____ to the _____; and to them that have no might He increaseth strength." Isaiah 40:29.

"_____ _____, the same, _____, and _____, and _____." Hebrews 13:8.

"My God shall _____ all your _____ according to His _____ in _____ by Christ Jesus." Philippians 4:19.

"_____ unto me, and I will _____thee." Jeremiah 33:3.

"Thou wilt keep him in _____ _____, whose _____ is stayed on Thee, because he trusteth in Thee." Isaiah 26:3.

"God is my _____ I will trust, and not be _____." Isaiah 12:2.

```
L W E C A E P T C E F R E P N
L J E S U S C H R I S T P C C
E K A S R O F A S Z Y U F F O
A H P C U S D E Y A M S I D M
V I C R M R T T D E E N Q Y M
E M A A I D D R E H P E H S I
V G L N N Z E E E E R L D F T
E R L S D T D F T N A W O O S
V A V W S I F V S S G C A R E
U E H E A A T R U S T T F E D
A P Y R I G V P O W E R H V W
V P F N D L P A S S E T H E W
P A T S A L V A T I O N F R N
T O D A Y R O L G S R E T A W
T R A E H V C C Y R I C H E S
```

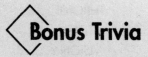

Bonus Trivia

At the end of the nineteenth century in America, there was one Protestant church per how many citizens?

450.

Jesus & John the Baptist

ANGEL	JOSEPH
BABE	JOY
BAPTIZE	LORD
BLESSED	MANGER
BLOOD	MARY
CALL	PEACE
COUSINS	PRIEST
CRUCIFY	REPENT
DOVE	SACRIFICE
ELISABETH	SALVATION
FORGIVENESS	SAVED
GABRIEL	SINS
GLORY	SON
GOD	SOUL
GREAT	STAR
HAIL	THE WAY
HAND	THRONE
HATH	TIME
HEARTS	VISION
HEROD	WATER
HIS	WOMB
HOLY GHOST	WORD
JESUS	ZACHARIAS

```
H M M B S G A B R I E L U O S
Z O V J L D O V E N O R H T M
E H L O W O R D J B A A S H H
M A R Y Y R O U O T N E L E T
F Y U F G E R D S D I H L W E
O L L I A H P E E R A M A A B
R L X C J N O S P T D N C Y A
G C O U S I N S H E M O G J S
I F G R E A T E T S N I S E I
V L U C D W Y L E M I T H S L
E E Z I T P A B A B E A E U E
N C L R E G N A M D E V A S G
E A I D S V I S I O N L R L Z
S E C I F I R C A S W A T E R
S P W Z A C H A R I A S S U M
```

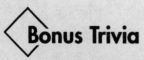

Bonus Trivia

After the Bible was divided into chapters,
how many years passed before it was divided
into verses?

300 (about A.D. 1250-1500).

Prophecies Fulfilled by Jesus

AROSE	NAZARENE
ASCEND	PARABLES
BETHLEHEM	PIERCED
BETRAYED	PRIEST
CORNERSTONE	REJECTED
CRUCIFIED	RULE
DAVID	SAD
EGYPT	SAVE
EMMANUEL	SCEPTER
ETERNAL	SCOURGED
FORSAKEN	SPIRIT
GIFTS	THIRST
GOD	THRONE
HEAL	VIRGIN
HIGH	WORSHIP
JUDAH	ZEAL

```
M D F D P T K S T H R O N E V
P E E O E I S D T L S A V E I
S A H Y R C H E I F A S A D R
Y C R E A S R S I V I E R D G
Y L O A L R A E R R A G H C I
A A T U B H T K I O P D O L N
D E H D R L T E E P W R E V R
E Z I N G G E E B N N U E E A
I T R E O J E S B E N N J L S
F I S L D N T D R A E E A C D
I R T U C H E S M R C N E N E
C I Z R A G T M A T R P E S H
U P U D Y O E Z E E T C O I T
R S U P N V A D T E S R G P T
C J T E V N I E R A A H B A K
```

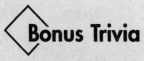

Bonus Trivia

In Dante's *Inferno,* who are held by Satan in the deepest pit?

Judas, Cassius, and Brutus (for being traitors).

Ordinary Objects Used by God in the Bible

DONKEY	LOINCLOTH
DUST	OIL
FIVE LOAVES BREAD	PIGS
FLEECE	POTTERY
FLIES	RAIN
FOOD	RIVERS
FROGS	ROD
HAIL	SLING
IRON PLATE	SMALL STONE
JARS	TORCHES
JAWBONE	TRUMPETS
LICE	TWO FISH
LOCUSTS	WATER

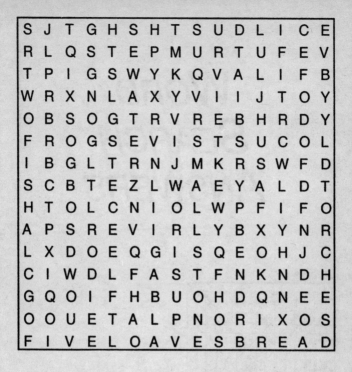

```
S J T G H S H T S U D L I C E
R L Q S T E P M U R T U F E V
T P I G S W Y K Q V A L I F B
W R X N L A X Y V I I J T O Y
O B S O G T R V R E B H R D Y
F R O G S E V I S T S U C O L
I B G L T R N J M K R S W F D
S C B T E Z L W A E Y A L D T
H T O L C N I O L W P F I F O
A P S R E V I R L Y B X Y N R
L X D O E Q G I S Q E O H J C
C I W D L F A S T F N K N D H
G Q O I F H B U O H D Q N E E
O O U E T A L P N O R I X O S
F I V E L O A V E S B R E A D
```

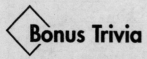

Bonus Trivia

"One short sleep past, we wake eternally,
And death shall be no more; death, thou
shalt die." Who is the author of this sonnet?

John Donne.

WORD
SEARCH
ANSWERS

Puzzle 1

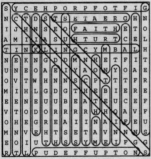

Puzzle 2

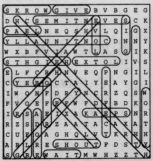

Puzzle 3

Puzzle 4

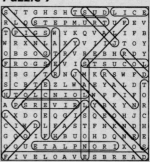

Puzzle 5

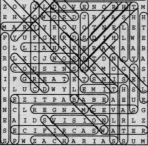

Puzzle 6

Puzzle 7

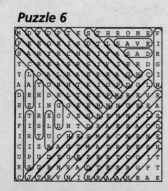

GREAT QUOTES ON PRAYER

Adoration sets the tone for the entire prayer.
It reminds us whom we are addressing,
whose presence we have entered,
whose attention we have gained.

BILL HYBELS
Too Busy Not To Pray

~

Let me call attention to that prayer of David,
in which he says: "Search me, O, God,
and know my heart. . . ."
If we should all honestly make this prayer
once every day there would be a good deal
of change in our lives.
"Search *me*"—not my neighbor.

D. L. MOODY
Prevailing Prayer

~

Prayers are heard in heaven
very much in proportion to our faith.
Little faith will get very great mercies,
but great faith still greater.

CHARLES H. SPURGEON
Gleanings Among the Sheaves: Believing Prayer

GREAT QUOTES ON PRAYER

I can worry myself into a state
of spiritual ennui over questions like
"What good does it do to pray
if God already knows everything?"
Jesus silences such questions.
He prayed, so should we.

PHILIP YANCEY
The Jesus I Never Knew

❧

True prayer is not to be found in the words of the mouth
but in the thoughts of the heart.

GREGORY THE GREAT
Commentary on the Book of Job

❧

Pray so that there is a real continuity between
your prayer and your whole actual life.

P. T. FORSYTH
The Soul of Prayer

GREAT QUOTES ON FAITH

Belief is truth held in the mind;
faith is a fire in the heart.

JOSEPH FORT NEWTON

~

Faith is putting all of your eggs into God's basket and
counting your blessings before they've hatched.

~

This is faith,
the renouncing of everything
we are apt to call our own
and relying wholly upon the blood,
righteousness, and intercession of Jesus.

JOHN NEWTON

~

"Though He slay me, yet will I trust Him"
—this is the most sublime utterance
of faith in the whole Bible.

OSWALD CHAMBERS

~

Faith is our spiritual oxygen. It not only keeps us alive in
God, but enables us to grow stronger.

JOYCE LANDORF HEATHERLY
The Inheritance

GREAT QUOTES ON FAITH

Faith is the gaze of a soul upon a saving God.

A. W. TOZER

~

Faith is deliberate confidence in the character of God
whose ways you may not understand at the time.

~

God requires a faithful fulfillment
of the merest trifle given us to do,
rather than the most ardent aspiration
to things to which we are not called.

FRANCIS DE SALES

~

It is useless to pray for more knowledge,
power, or faith until you begin to use
what you have already.

HENRY BUCKLEW
Your Daily Spiritual Vitamins

~

Faith is not belief without proof
but trust without reservation.

ELTON TRUEBLOOD

GREAT QUOTES ON LOVE

To be able to say how much you love
is to love but little.

PATRARCH

~

"Love thy neighbor" is a precept
which could transform the world
if it were universally practiced.

MARY MCLEOD BETHUNE

~

No love, no friendship,
can cross the path of our destiny
without leaving some mark on it forever.

FRANCOIS MAURIAC

~

Life with Christ is endless love;
Without Him it is a loveless end.

BILLY GRAHAM

~

Love is the lesson which the
Lord taught us.

EDMUND SPENCER

GREAT QUOTES ON LOVE

Love is the greatest thing that God can give us,
for Himself is love;
and it is the greatest things we can give to God,
for it will also give ourselves.

JEREMY TAYLOR

~

The measure of God's love
is that he loves without measure.

ST. BERNARD

~

Love is an image of God,
and not a lifeless image,
but the living essence of the divine nature
which beams full of all goodness.

MARTIN LUTHER

~

Riches take wings; comforts vanish; hope withers away,
but love stays with us. God is love.

LEW WALLACE

~

Love seeks to make happy rather than to be happy.

RALPH CONNER

Great Quotes on Grace

Grace is the free,
undeserved goodness and favour
of God to mankind.

Matthew Henry

~

Grace is the soul of the gospel:
without it the gospel is dead.
Grace is the music of the gospel:
without it the gospel is silent as to all comfort.

Charles H. Spurgeon
The Doctrines of Grace Do Not Lead to Sin

~

From faith to faith,
from grace to grace,
So in Thy strength shall I go on,
Till heaven and earth flee from Thy face,
And glory end what grace begun.

Wolfgang Christoph Dessler
"Into Thy Gracious Hands I Fall"

~

Grace is but glory begun,
and glory is but grace perfected.

Jonathan Edwards

COUPON EXPIRES: 10-31-02

Consumer: Coupon redeemable at Bible Factory Outlet locations only. Good on regular price of in-stock item. Limit one coupon per customer. Not valid with any other offer. No cash value.

BIBLE FACTORY OUTLET

Retailer: Redeem five $2-off coupons to receive one free CD from Provident Music Distribution. Valid on any product. Provident Music Distribution, 741 Cool Springs Blvd. Franklin, TN 37067

0 99900 13870 8

COUPON EXPIRES: 10-31-02

Consumer: Coupon redeemable at Bible Factory Outlet locations only. Good on regular price of in-stock item. Limit one coupon per customer. Not valid with any other offer. No cash value.

BIBLE FACTORY OUTLET

Retailer: Redeem five $2-off coupons to receive one free CD from Provident Music Distribution. Valid on any product. Provident Music Distribution, 741 Cool Springs Blvd. Franklin, TN 37067

0 99900 13888 3

COUPON EXPIRES: 10-31-02

Consumer: Coupon redeemable at Bible Factory Outlet locations only. Good on regular price of in-stock item. Limit one coupon per customer. Not valid with any other offer. No cash value.

BIBLE FACTORY OUTLET

Retailer: Redeem five $2-off coupons to receive one free CD from Provident Music Distribution. Valid on any product. Provident Music Distribution, 741 Cool Springs Blvd. Franklin, TN 37067

0 99900 13896 8

COUPON EXPIRES: 10-31-02

Consumer: Coupon redeemable at Bible Factory Outlet locations only. Good on regular price of in-stock item. Limit one coupon per customer. Not valid with any other offer. No cash value.

BIBLE FACTORY OUTLET

Retailer: Redeem five $2-off coupons to receive one free CD from Provident Music Distribution. Valid on any product. Provident Music Distribution, 741 Cool Springs Blvd. Franklin, TN 37067

0 99900 13901 9

$3.00 OFF ANY
SONGS4WORSHIP

CD or Cassette with this coupon

Featuring 22 songs of Christmas worship, this "as seen on TV" collection is sure to bring the joy of the Christmas season into your home, office or car. From the sounds of Darlene Zschech singing Silent Night and her new song, Hallelujah, to the traditional sounds of Joy To the Word and O Holy Night, Songs4Worship Christmas will be a treasure this Christmas time.

$2.00 OFF ANY
SHOUT TO THE LORD KIDS!

CD or Cassette with this coupon

The vibrant sounds of children worshiping the God of Gods and Lord of Lords will resound in your heart as you listen to Shout To The Lord Kids 2. Recorded live at the North Point Community Church in North Atlanta, this children's worship album features some of the great modern worship songs of today that will delight kids of all ages.

$2.00 OFF
SONICFLOOd RESONATE

CD or Cassette with this coupon

From the band that redefined praise and worship comes the all new studio album RESONATE. RESONATE features a mixture of well known modern praise songs and powerful originals written by SONICFLOOd. This album of modern worship is intended to usher you into the presence of God.

$2.00 OFF ANY
LITTLE DOGS ON THE PRAIRIE

Kids Video with this coupon

Set in the Old (but not too old) West, Little Dogs on the Prairie is a new video series done in classic cell-animation style, with 35 minutes of zany fun, great songs, and well-told stories teaching Biblically-based values like humility, honesty, and love from a Christian perspective.

COUPON EXPIRES: 10-31-02

Customer: Coupon redeemable at Bible Factory Outlet locations only. Please present this coupon for $3 off the purchase of any regularly priced, in-stock Songs4Worship cassette or compact disc. Sales tax may apply. Limit one coupon per customer per visit. This voucher has no cash value and may not be combined with any other offer. May not be copied or transferred.

BIBLE FACTORY OUTLET

Retailer: Redeem coupon as one (1) "1-free-with-4" coupon with Word Distribution by January 31, 2003. [Retailer receives one free CD from Word Distribution for every 5 coupons redeemed.] Coupon must be redeemed for redemption.

0 99900 13934 7

COUPON EXPIRES: 10-31-02

Customer: Coupon redeemable at Bible Factory Outlet locations only. Please present this coupon for $2 off the purchase of any regularly priced, in-stock Shout to the Lord Kids! cassette or compact disc. Sales tax may apply. Limit one coupon per customer per visit. This voucher has no cash value and may not be combined with any other offer. May not be copied or transferred.

BIBLE FACTORY OUTLET

Retailer: Redeem coupon as one (1) "1-free-with-4" coupon with Word Distribution by January 31, 2003. [Retailer receives one free CD from Word Distribution for every 5 coupons redeemed.] Coupon must be redeemed for redemption.

0 99900 13942 2

COUPON EXPIRES: 10-31-02

Customer: Coupon redeemable at Bible Factory Outlet locations only. Please present this coupon for $2 off the purchase of any regularly priced, in-stock SONICFLOOd - RESONATE cassette or compact disc. Sales tax may apply. Limit one coupon per customer per visit. This voucher has no cash value and may not be combined with any other offer. May not be copied or transferred.

BIBLE FACTORY OUTLET

Retailer: Redeem coupon as one (1) "1-free-with-4" coupon with Word Distribution by January 31, 2003. [Retailer receives one free CD from Word Distribution for every 5 coupons redeemed.] Coupon must be redeemed for redemption.

0 99900 13950 7

COUPON EXPIRES: 10-31-02

Customer: Coupon redeemable at Bible Factory Outlet locations only. Please present this coupon for $2 off the purchase of any regularly priced, in-stock Little Dogs on the Prairie Video. Sales tax may apply. Limit one coupon per customer per visit. This voucher has no cash value and may not be combined with any other offer. May not be copied or transferred.

BIBLE FACTORY OUTLET

Retailer: Redeem coupon as 50% of face value with Thomas Nelson Publishers by January 31, 2003. $1.00 will be credited to your account for each coupon returned to your Sales Rep. Coupon must be redeemed for redemption.

0 99900 13977 4